HÄGAR

THE HORRIBLE

THE BRUTISH
ARE COMING #4

BY DIK BROWNE

tempo
books

GROSSET & DUNLAP
A Filmways Company
Publishers • New York

7-18

HAMLET, MY SON, BOOK LEARNING IS OKAY, I GUESS... BUT—

IT WON'T HELP YOU OUT THERE IN THE *REAL* WORLD WITH YOUR DAY-TO-DAY PROBLEMS.

DIK BROWNE

LIKE WITCHES, TROLLS, PIXIES, DEMONS...

I'VE INVENTED THE MARTINI — NOW I MUST PERFECT IT...

IT NEEDS A FRUIT OF SOME KIND — BUT WHICH?

I'LL DO IT ALPHABETICALLY—

WELL, IT ISN'T A BANANA...

BEFORE I TELL THIS ONE—CAN YOU TAKE A JOKE?

OH, I CAN TAKE A JOKE AS WELL AS THE NEXT GUY.

IN THAT CASE— FORGET IT!!

DIK BROWNE 12-12